I Feel Shy

Written by Karen Bryant-Mole

Illustrated by Mike Gordon

sundance

Kid-to-Kid Books

Red Set	Green Set	Blue Set	Yellow Set
I Feel Angry	I Feel Bored	I Feel Bullied	Excuse Me!
I Feel Happy	I Feel Jealous	I Feel Frightened	I Don't Care!
I Feel Lonely	I Feel Shy	I Feel Sad	I'll Do It!
It's Not Fair	I Feel Worried	Why Wash?	It Wasn't Me!

Copyright © 1999 Sundance Publishing

No part of this publication may be reproduced,
stored in a retrieval system or transmitted
in any form or by any other means, electronic,
mechanical, photocopying, recording or otherwise,
without the prior written permission of the publisher.

All rights reserved.
This edition published
in North America by
Sundance Publishing
P.O. Box 1326
234 Taylor Street
Littleton, MA 01460

First published in 1998 by
Wayland Publishers Limited

Copyright © 1998 Wayland Publishers Limited

ISBN 0-7608-3919-0

Printed in Canada

In the corner today,
we're talking about

feeling shy.

This way to Kids Corner

3

When I feel shy,
I feel like

a flower that doesn't
want to open,

a baby chick
hiding under
its mother's wing,

a quiet triangle in a loud band.

When I feel shy,
my face turns red,

6

and my legs and tummy feel wobbly.

When I feel shy,

sometimes I am very quiet,

sometimes I giggle.

But it isn't a happy sort of giggle.
It's a worried sort of giggle.

When the teacher asks me a question,
I feel shy.

I worry that I might
get the answer wrong
or say something silly.
Then everyone might laugh at me.

When I'm in a play at school,
I feel shy.

But when everyone claps,
I feel proud of myself.

When I go to parties,
I sometimes feel shy.
I don't want to play the party games.

But, after a while,
I stop feeling so shy.
When I see how much fun
my friends are having, I join in, too.

When I visit Great-Aunt Maud,
I feel shy.

But I stop feeling shy
when she asks me if I would like
to help her make some cookies.

Sometimes grown-ups feel shy, too.

My mom feels shy
when she goes to a party
and doesn't know anyone else there.

19

My teacher says he felt shy on his wedding day, because he knew everyone would be looking at him.

Grown-ups sometimes feel shy
when they meet important people
or famous people.

When I feel shy,
I wish I were a magician.

Then I could make
myself invisible.

POOF!

When I feel shy,
it helps if people smile
at me.

Do you know someone who sometimes feels shy?

What could you do to help?

Things to Do in the Kids Corner

Shy people are also called "shrinking violets." Draw a small violet on a piece of paper. On other pieces of paper, draw bigger and bigger violets. Staple the papers together, smallest to biggest. Flip through and see your violet shrink. (Flip the other way and see it grow!)

Make two finger puppets. Name them Shy Shelly and Friendly Frank. Put on a puppet show about how Frank helps Shelly make friends on her first day at a new school.

List as many words as you can think of that rhyme with *shy*. Challenge a friend to do the same. Use the rhyming words to make up a poem about being shy.

30

To feel less shy when you meet new people, make a ME tag. On an index card write, *Hi! My name is* ___. Draw pictures of things you like to do. You can also write things like, *My favorite color is* ___, or *I have a pet* ___.

Draw a comic strip about someone who was feeling shy. Show why he or she was feeling shy and what he or she did to feel less shy.

my dog

Spot

my house

Other Books to Read

Angel Child, Dragon Child, by Michele Maria Surat (Scholastic Books, 1989). Ut has just come to America from Vietnam without her mother. She does not like her new school. Will she reach out to make new friends? *35 pages*

Crow Boy, by Taro Yashima (Penguin Books, 1983). A shy mountain boy in Japan leaves his home at dawn to go to the village school. *36 pages*

At the Park, by Peter Sloan and Sheryl Sloan (a Sundance *Little Red Reader*, 1995). Sometimes when you feel shy, you just want to be alone. Read about the nice day one girl had by herself. *8 pages*

Sebastian, by Sarah Prince (a Sundance *AlphaKids Guided Reader*, 1999). Every morning Sebastian felt like crying. Then one day, he met Isabella. Now Sebastian likes to go to school. *16 pages*

Chang's Paper Pony, by Eleanor Coerr (HarperCollins, 1993). Chang and his grandfather leave China and come to California during the gold rush. Chang is unable to make new friends and dreams of having a pony as his friend. *64 pages*

Children at Play, by Peter Sloan and Sheryl Sloan (a Sundance *Little Red Reader*, 1996). Having fun things to do helps you make friends. Here are ideas for fun things to do with other kids. *8 pages*

We Are Best Friends, by Aliki (Morrow, 1987). Robert and Peter are best friends until Peter moves away. Another best friend is hard to find. *30 pages*